MICKEY MOUSE CLUBHOUSE

NUMBERS

& COUNTING
Learning Workbook

- **Number Concepts**

- **Identify and Count Numbers 1 - 20**

- **Fun Learning Activities**

BENDON™

Bendon Publishing Int'l, Inc.
Ashland, OH 44805
www.bendonpub.com

Disney Junior

Number 1

What number is Mickey climbing?

Mickey is climbing the number **one**.
Trace the number **1** and word below. Then, practice writing it on your own.

NUMBERS & COUNTING

© Disney

Number 2

Minnie loves to shop. Color the bags with the number **2** inside.

Minnie has **two** purses.
Trace the number **2** and word below. Then, practice writing it on your own.

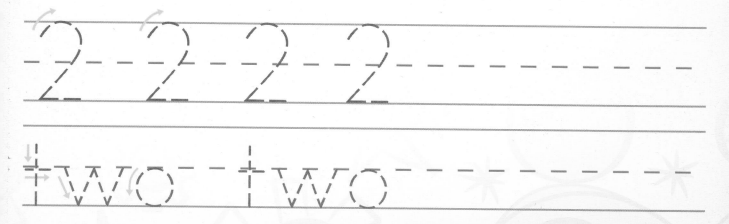

NUMBERS & COUNTING

© Disney

Number 3

Can you find the number **3** throughout the picture below? Circle each one. There are seven.

There are **three** windows on Mickey's camper.
Trace the number **3** and word below. Then, practice writing it on your own.

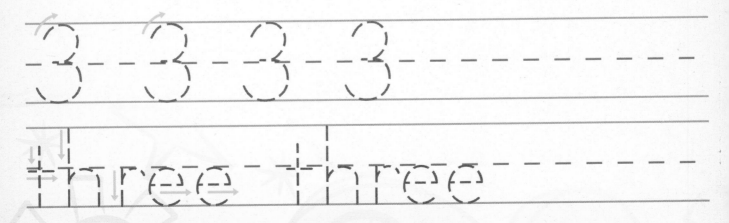

3 3 3 3

three three

4

NUMBERS & COUNTING

Number 4

Mickey loves to play soccer. Circle the soccer balls that have the number **4** on them.

There are **four** soccer balls with the number **4** on them.
Trace the number **4** and word below. Then, practice writing it on your own.

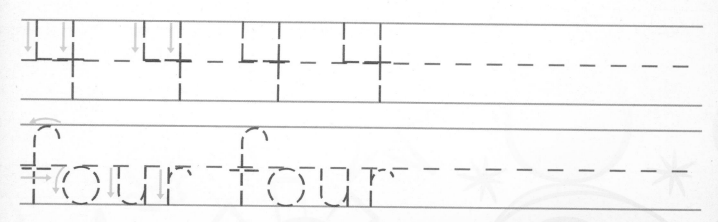

NUMBERS & COUNTING

© Disney

Number 5

Count the large ears of corn below.
How many did you count?

There are **five** large ears of corn.
Trace the number **5** and word below. Then, practice writing it on your own.

5 5 5 5

five five

NUMBERS & COUNTING

© Disney

Number 6

Minnie loves shoes. Circle the shoes that have a number **6** on them.

There are **six** blue shoes.
Trace the number **6** and word below. Then, practice writing it on your own.

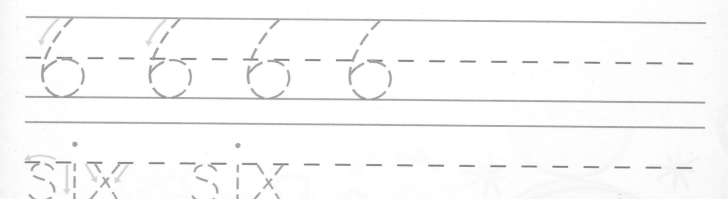

6 6 6 6

six six

NUMBERS & COUNTING

7

Number 7

Put an **X** on the oranges with a number 6.
Circle the oranges with a number **7**.
How many oranges have a number **7**?

Five oranges have the number **seven**.
Trace the number **7** and word below. Then, practice writing it on your own.

NUMBERS & COUNTING

Number
8

Pluto loves playing with butterflies.
How many butterflies can you count?

There are **eight** butterflies.
Trace the number **8** and word below. Then, practice writing it on your own.

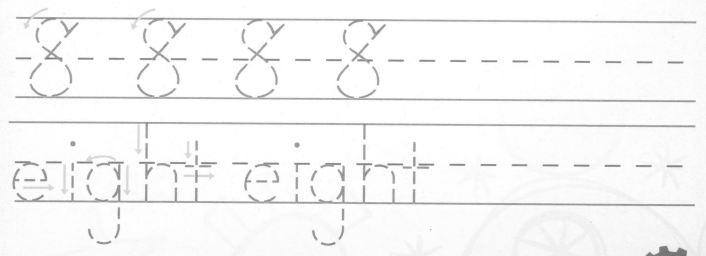

NUMBERS & COUNTING

© Disney

Number 9

Help Daisy count the bows. How many are there?

There are **nine** bows.
Trace the number **9** and word below. Then, practice writing it on your own.

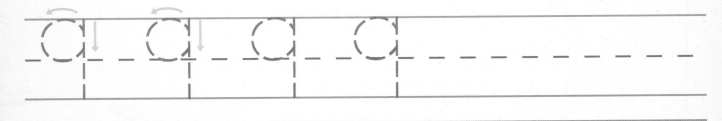

a a a a

nine nine

NUMBERS & COUNTING

© Disney

Number
10

Help Goofy fill his empty fruit bowl.
Count the apples.
Now, count the bananas.
How many pieces of fruit are there altogether?

There are **ten** pieces of fruit altogether.
Trace the number **10** and word below. Then, practice writing it on your own.

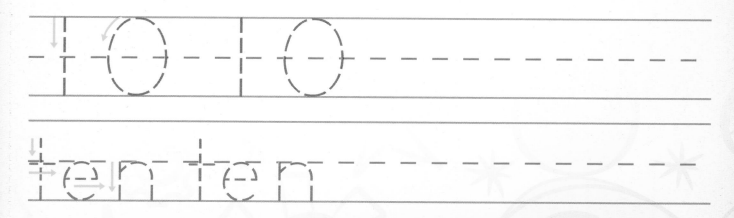

Number
11

Fill in the missing numbers below. Then, follow the directions.

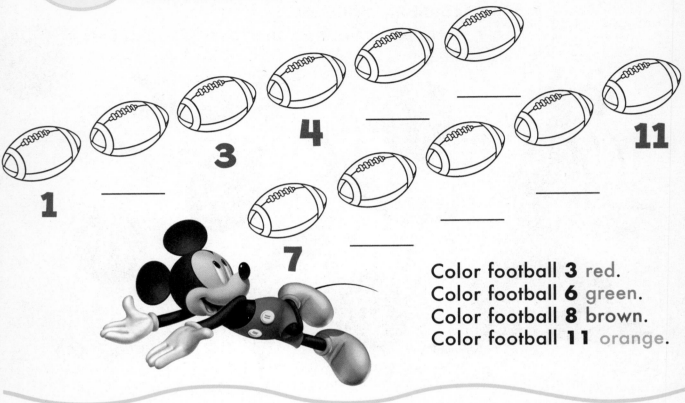

1   **3**   **4**   **7**   **11**

Color football **3** red.
Color football **6** green.
Color football **8** brown.
Color football **11** orange.

There are **eleven** footballs.
Trace the number **11** and word below. Then, practice writing it on your own.

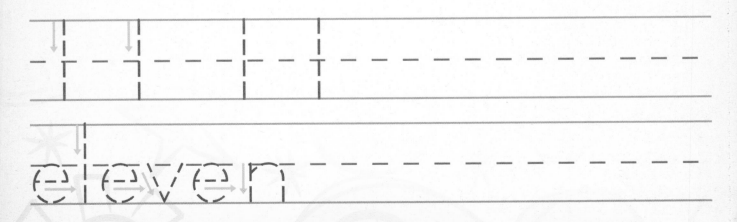

eleven

© Disney

Number 12

Help Donald count all the soccer balls below. How many soccer balls are there?

Donald has **twelve** soccer balls.
Trace the number **12** and word below. Then, practice writing it on your own.

12 12

twelve

NUMBERS & COUNTING

Number 13

How many rubber ducks do you see?
Help Pluto count them.

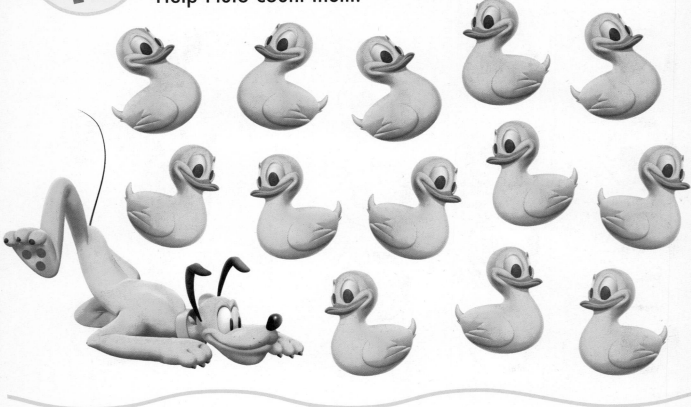

There are **thirteen** rubber duckies.
Trace the number **13** and word below. Then, practice writing it on your own.

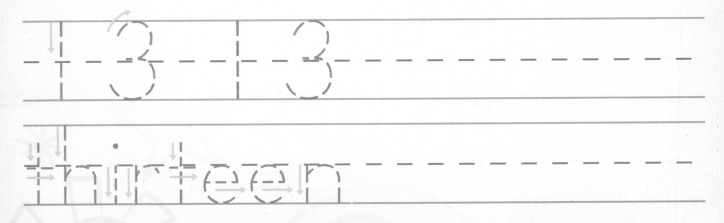

NUMBERS & COUNTING

Number 14

Daisy loves flowers. Circle the flowers that have the number **14** in them.

There are three flowers with the number **fourteen**.
Trace the number **14** and word below. Then, practice writing it on your own.

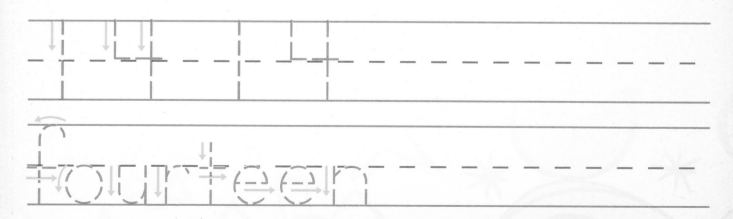

NUMBERS & COUNTING

Number
15

Can you finish the picture of Daisy below?
Connect the dots from 1 to **15**.

Trace the number **15** and word below. Then, practice writing it on your own.

15   15

fifteen

NUMBERS & COUNTING

© Disney

Number 16

Help Donald through the maze. Follow the number **16** to the center.

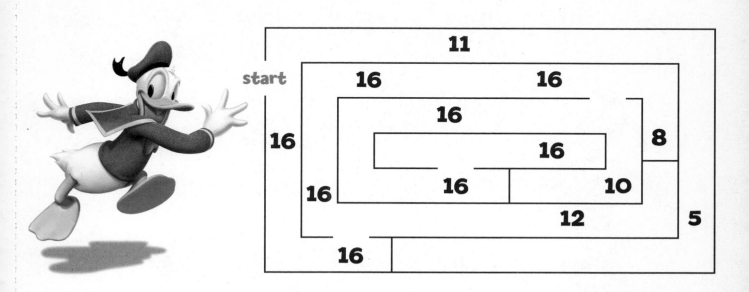

Trace the number **16** and word below. Then, practice writing it on your own.

16   16 - - - - - - -

sixteen - - - - -

NUMBERS & COUNTING

© Disney

Number 17

Help Goofy count the puppies. How many are there?

There are **seventeen** puppies.
Trace the number **17** and word below. Then, practice writing it on your own.

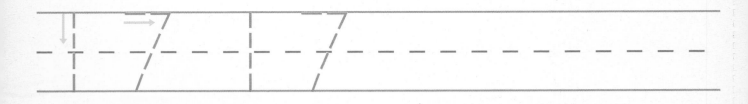

NUMBERS & COUNTING

© Disney

Number
18

How many cats do you see below?
Count them.

There are **eighteen** cats.
Trace the number **18** and word below. Then, practice writing it on your own.

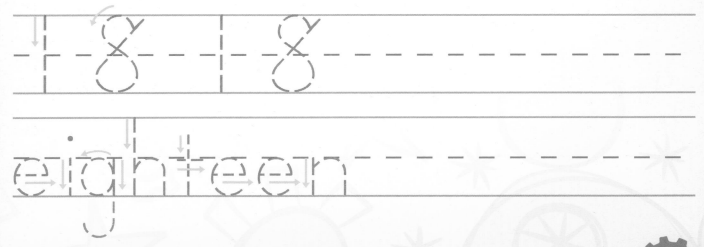

NUMBERS & COUNTING

© Disney

Number 19

Count the radios below. How many are there?

There are **nineteen** radios.
Trace the number **19** and word below. Then, practice writing it on your own.

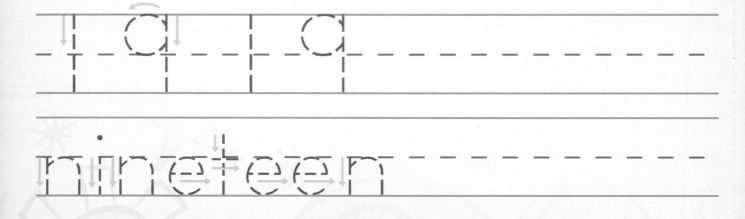

NUMBERS & COUNTING

© Disney

Number 20

Count the sheep below. How many are there?

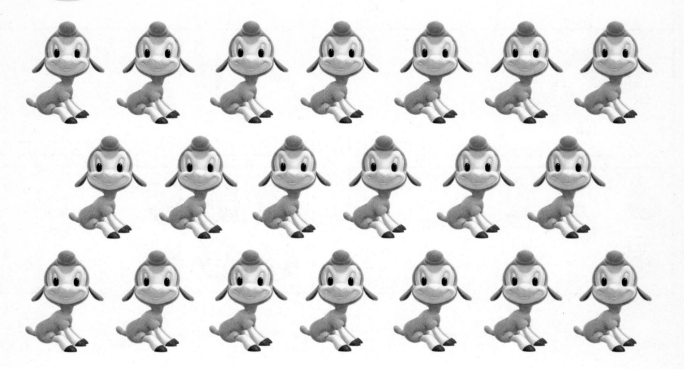

There are **twenty** sheep.
Trace the number **20** and word below. Then, practice writing it on your own.

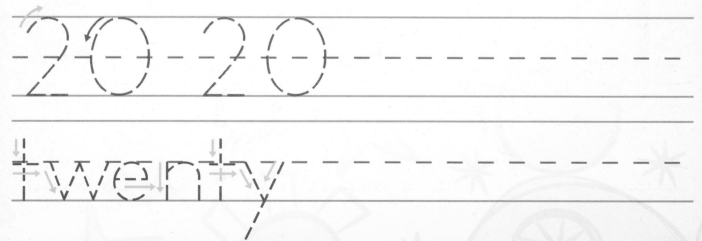

NUMBERS & COUNTING

© Disney

Counting 1-10

Count and write the number of objects you see in each box.

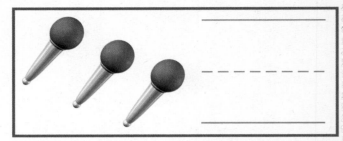

Write in the missing numbers below counting from **1** to **10**.

1 _____ 3 _____ 5

_____ 7 _____ 9 _____

NUMBERS & COUNTING

© Disney

Counting 11-15

Count and write the number of objects you see in each box.

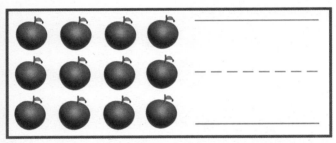 _____

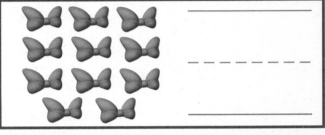 _____

 _____

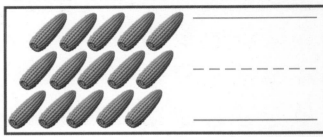 _____

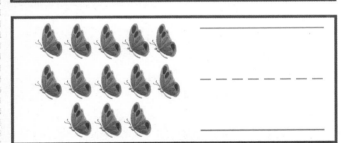 _____

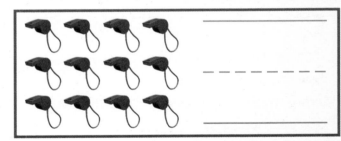 _____

Write in the missing numbers below counting from **11** to **15**.

11 _____ 13 _____ 15

Counting 16-20

Count and write the number of objects you see in each box.

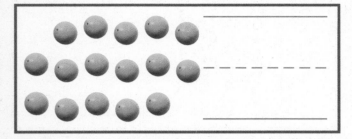

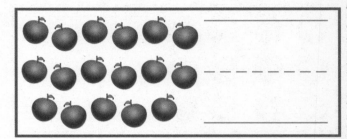

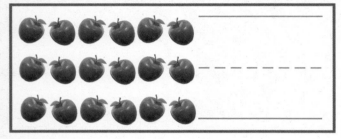

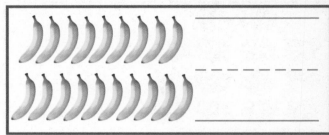

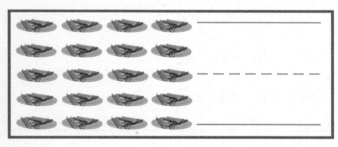

Fill in the missing numbers from **16** to **20**.

16 ___ 18 ___ ___

NUMBERS & COUNTING

Counting 1-20

Count from **1** to **20** by filling in the missing numbers below.

1 ___ 3 ___ 5

___ 7 ___ 9 ___

11 ___ 13 ___ 15

___ 17 ___ 19 ___

NUMBERS & COUNTING

Review 1-20

Follow the color code below to finish the picture.

Color 1, 2, 3 & 4 red
Color 5, 6, 7 & 8 orange
Color 9, 10 & 11 dark blue
Color 12 light blue

Color 13 & 14 pink
Color 15 & 16 yellow
Color 17 & 18 green
Color 19 & 20 brown

NUMBERS & COUNTING

Follow the directions above each box.

Circle the ball with the number **3**. Then, trace the number **3**.

Put an **X** on the number **4**. Then, trace the number **4**.

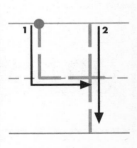

Draw a square around the number **5**. Then, trace the number **5**.

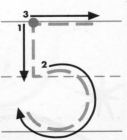

27

NUMBERS & COUNTING

Practice 1-20

Fill in the missing numbers. Then, follow the directions above each box.

Color ball 6 purple. Then, write the number 6.

(6) ( ) (8) ( ) ( ) (11)

- - - - - - -

Color ball 11 green. Then, write the number 11.

(10) ( ) ( ) (13) ( ) (15)

- - - - - - -

Color ball 20 orange. Then, write the number 20.

( ) (16) ( ) ( ) (19) ( )

- - - - - - -

28

NUMBERS & COUNTING

© Disney

Practice
1-20

Follow the directions above each box.

Write the missing number on the lines.

Write the missing number on the lines.

Write the missing number on the lines.

NUMBERS & COUNTING

Practice 1-20

Help Mickey find his way through the maze by counting from **1** to **20**.

1 2 3 4 5
6   6
7   7
8
11 10 9
12
13
12
14
13
20
15 16 17 18 19

NUMBERS & COUNTING

© Disney

Practice 1-20

Practice writing the numbers 1 to 20 below.

1

20

NUMBERS & COUNTING

CERTIFICATE OF COMPLETION

name

has hereby completed the

MICKEY MOUSE CLUBHOUSE

Numbers & Counting Workbook!

A JOB WELL DONE, PAL!!